LADIES & GENTLE

THE BEST OF GEORGE MICHAEL

Exclusive Distributors

International Music Publications Limited
Griffin House, 161 Hammersmith Road, London W6 8BS, England

International Music Publications GmbH, Germany
Marstallstraße 8, D-80539 Munchen, Germany

Nuova Carisch S.p.A.
Via Campania, 12 20098 S. Giuliano Milanese (MI)
Zona Industriale Sesto Ulteriano, Italy
20, rue de la Ville-l'Eveque-75008 Paris, France

Danmusik
Vognmagergade 7, DK-1120 Copenhagen K, Denmark

Warner/Chappell Music Australia Pty Ltd.
3 Talavera Road, North Ryde, New South Wales 2113, Australia

Folio © 1999 International Music Publications Ltd
Griffin House, 161 Hammersmith Road, London W6 8BS, England

for the heart

JESUS TO A CHILD

Words and Music by
George Michael

And what have I____ learned   from all____ this   pain?   I thought I'd   ne - ver   feel
And what have I____ learned   from all____ these   tears,   I've wait - ed   for__ you   all__

__ the same   a - bout   a - ny - one__   or   a - ny-thing a - gain.
__ those   years,   but   just   when it   be-gan,   he   took your love   a - way.

__   But   now   I   know   when you find____ love,__ when you know_____ that it__ ex - ists,
__   But   I   still   say   when you find____ love,__ when you know_____ that it__ ex - ists,

__   then the   lov - er   that__ you   miss____   will   come to__ you   on   those

FATHER FIGURE

Words and Music by
George Michael

That's all I want-ed some-thing spe-cial, some-thing

VERSE 3:
That's all I wanted
But sometimes love can be mistaken
For a crime
That's all I wanted
Just to see my baby's blue eyes shine.

This time I think that my lover understands me
If we have faith in each other
Then we can be strong baby.

CARELESS WHISPER

Words and Music by
George Michael and Andrew Ridgeley

1. I feel so un-sure as I
2. Time can ne-ver mend the
3. (To)-night the music seems so loud, I wish that we could lose this crowd,

take your hand and lead you to the dance floor;
care-less whis-per of a good friend;
may-be it's bet-ter this way, if we'd hurt each oth-er with the things we want to say. We

DON'T LET THE SUN GO DOWN ON ME

Words and Music by
Elton John and Bernie Taupin

24

YOU HAVE BEEN LOVED

Words and Music by
George Michael and David Austin

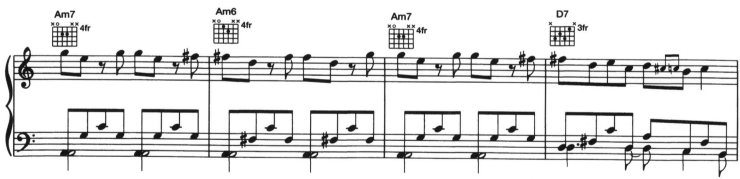

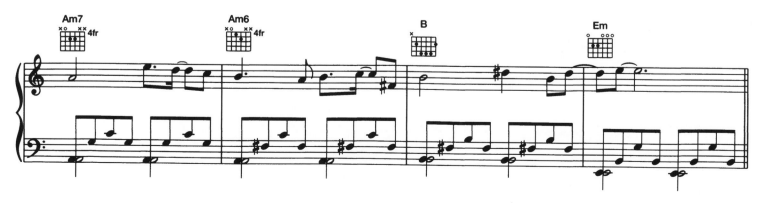

KISSING A FOOL

Words and Music by
George Michael

34

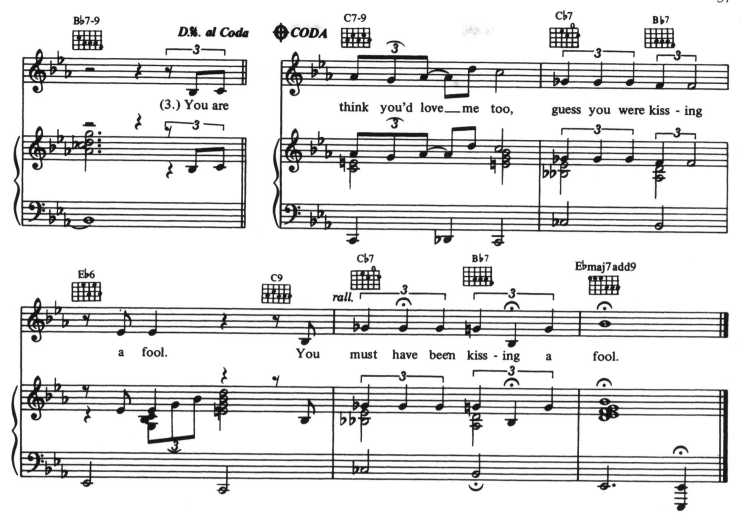

VERSE 2:
You are far
I'm never gonna be your star
I'll pick up the pieces and mend my heart
Maybe I'll be strong enough
I don't know where to start
But I'll never find peace of mind
While I listen to my heart.
People you can never change the way they feel
Better let them do just what they will
For they will
If you let them steal your heart.
People
Will always make a lover feel a fool
But you knew I loved you
We could have shown you all la la la la la la.

VERSE 3:
You are far
When I could have been your star
You listened to people
Who scared you to death and from my heart
Strange that I was wrong enough
To think you'd love me too
Guess you were kissing a fool
You must have been kissing a fool.

I CAN'T MAKE YOU LOVE ME

Words and Music by
Mike Reid and Allen Shamblin

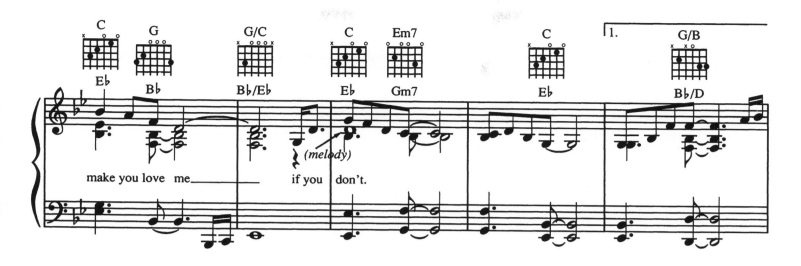

make you love me_____ if you don't.

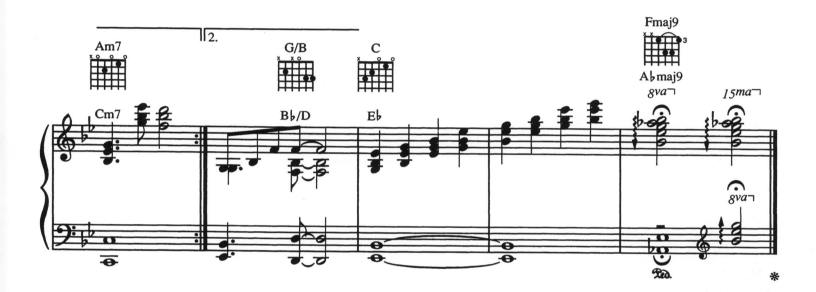

Verse 2:
I'll close my eyes, then I won't see
The love you don't feel when you're holdin' me.
Mornin' will come and I'll do what's right.
Just give me till then to give up this fight.
And I will give up this fight.
(To Chorus:)

HEAL THE PAIN

Words and Music by
George Michael

A MOMENT WITH YOU

Words and Music by
George Michael

DESAFINADO

Words and Music by
Antonio Carlos Jobim and Newton Ferriera de Mendonca

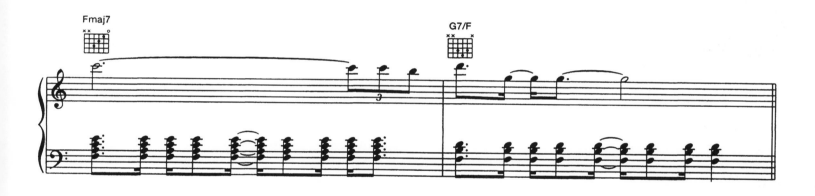

Se vo - cê dis - ser___ que eu de - sa - fi - no a - mor,___ yeah,

ASTRUD GILBERTO

Vo - cê__ com a su - a mu - si - ca__ es que__ ceu o prin - ci - pal,__ que no

pei - to dos de - sa - fi - na - dos no fun - do do pei - to ba - te ca - la do,__ no

pei - to dos de - sa - fi - na - dos tam - bem ba - te um co - ra - coa.__

repeat ad lib. to fade

COWBOYS AND ANGELS

Words and Music by
George Michael

74

please be strong-er than your past   the fut-ure may still give you

a chance

PRAYING FOR TIME

Words and Music by
George Michael

ONE MORE TRY

Words and Music by
George Michael

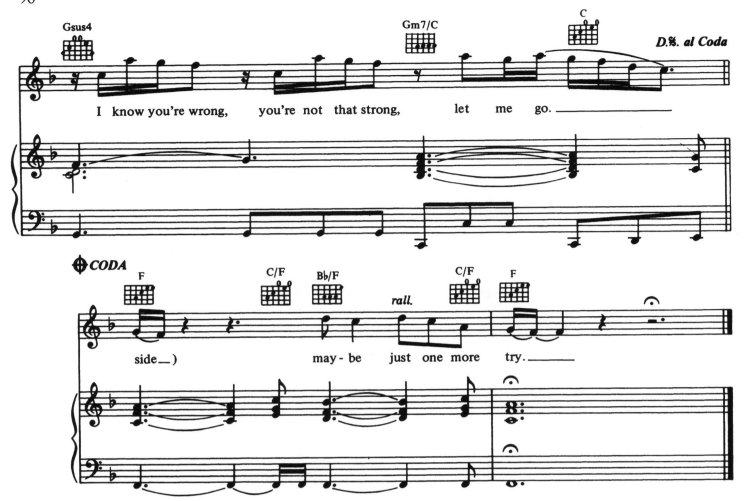

VERSE 2:

When you were just a stranger
And I was at your feet
I didn't feel the danger
Now I feel the heat
That look in your eyes
Telling me no
So you think that you love me
Know that you need me
I wrote the song, I know it's wrong
Just let me go . . .

D.S.

And teacher
There are things
That I still have to learn
But the one thing I have is my pride
Oh so I don't want to learn to
Hold you, touch you
Think that you're mine
Because there ain't no joy
For an uptown boy
Who just isn't willing to try
I'm so cold
Inside.

A DIFFERENT CORNER

Words and Music by
George Michael

To Coda ◆

I'm so scared,_____ { I'm so scared. of this love.

Take_ me back in time, may-be I can for - get,_ turn_ a diff - 'rent corn - er and we nev - er would_ have

for the feet

OUTSIDE

Words and Music by
George Michael

AS

Words and Music by
Stevie Wonder

FASTLOVE

Words and Music by
George Michael

TOO FUNKY

Words and Music by
George Michael

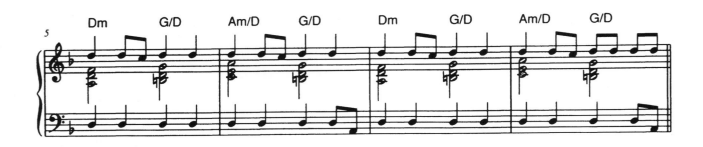

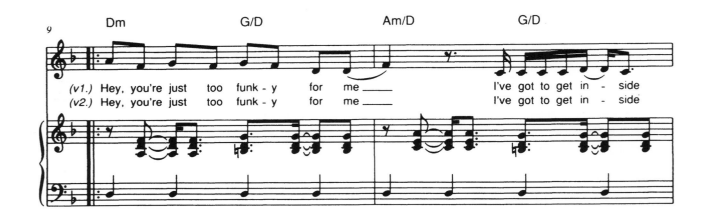

(v1.) Hey, you're just too funk-y for me ___ I've got to get in - side
(v2.) Hey, you're just too funk-y for me ___ I've got to get in - side

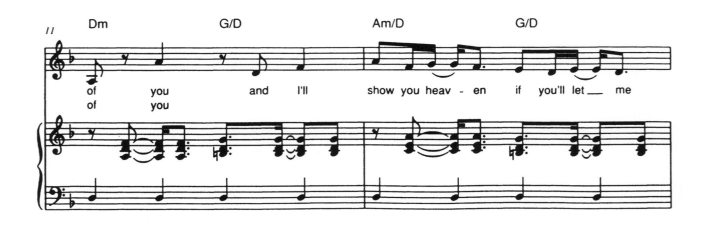

of you and I'll show you heav - en if you'll let ___ me
of you

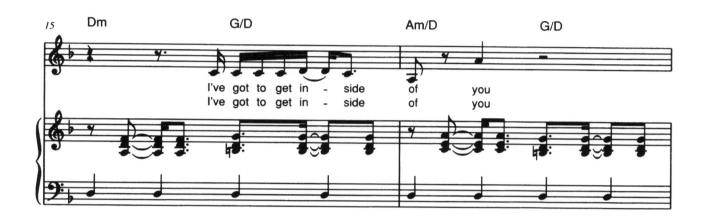

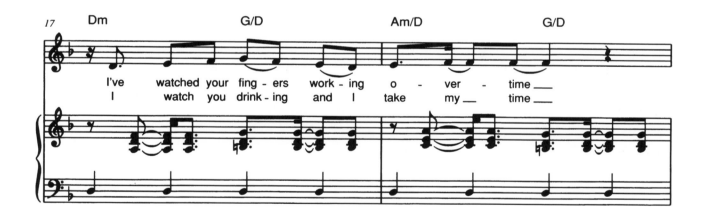

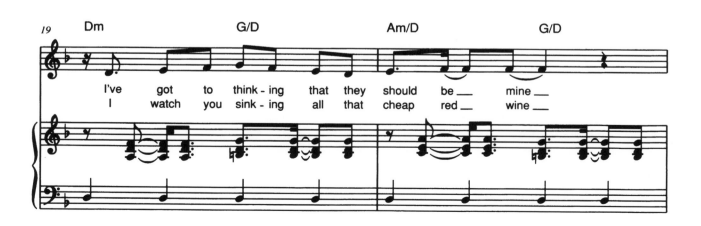

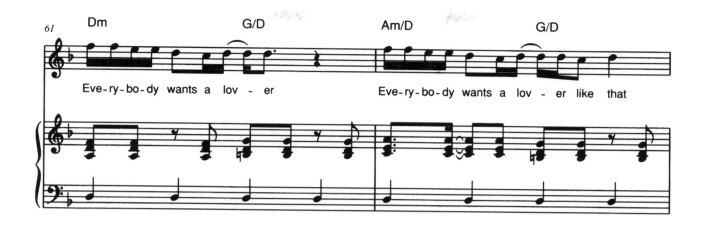

Ny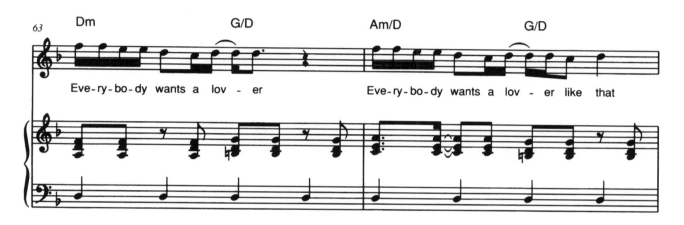

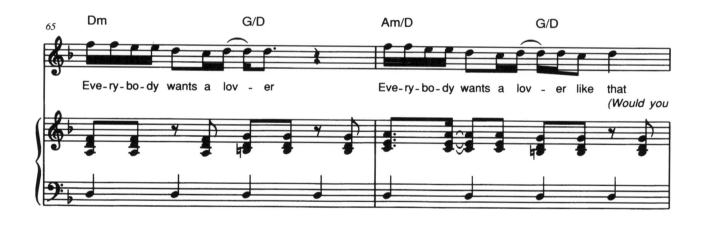

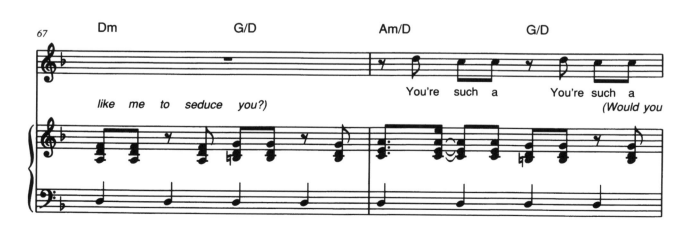

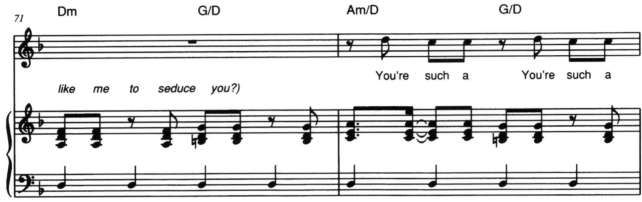

("Would you stop playing with that Radio of yours. I'm trying to get to sleep!")

FREEDOM 90

Words and Music by
George Michael

(Tempo ♩ = 90)

I won't let you down ___ I will not give you up ___ got to have some faith in the sound ___ It's the one good thing that I've got I won't let you down ___ so please don't give me up ___

130

134

142

Repeat to fade

STAR PEOPLE

Words and Music by
George Michael

Maybe your ma-ma gave you up___ boy.

Maybe your dad-dy did-n't love you e-nough girl.___

146

KILLER/PAPA WAS A ROLLING STONE

Words and Music by
Sealhenri Samuel and Adam Tinley

Words and Music by
Norman Whitfield and Barrett Strong

him, no, ___ ne - ver heard no-thin' but bad ___ things a - bout ___ him.

Ma-ma I'm de-pend-ing on you ___ to tell me the truth. ___ My

Ma-ma just hung her head and said: ___ Pa - pa was a roll - in' stone, ___ yeah,

wher-ev - er he laid his hat was his home. *And when he died,* ___ *all* ___

I WANT YOUR SEX (Part II)

Words and Music by
George Michael

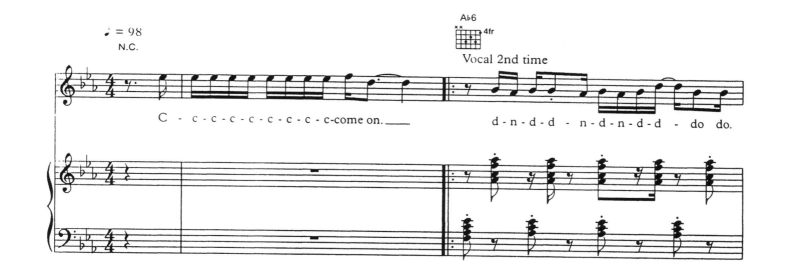

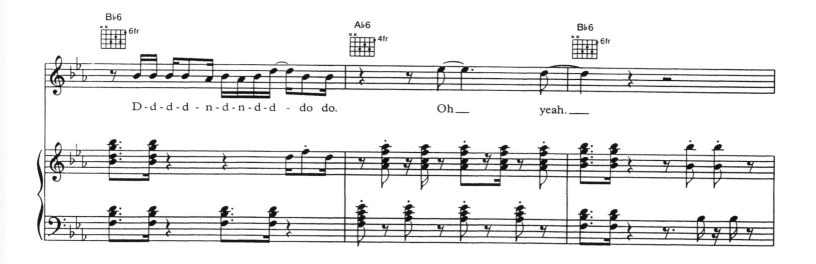

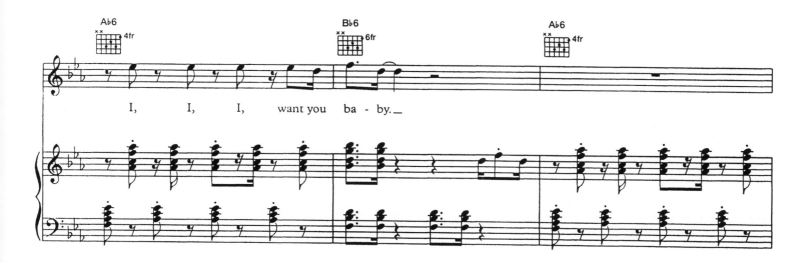

you and_____ me._____ Ow!

I want your . . .

THE STRANGEST THING

Words and Music by
George Michael

(2nd time only) La___ la la la___ la la la___ la___ la   la___ la la la la___ la

la la___ la___ la   la la la la.___

172

FANTASY

Words and Music by
George Michael

SPINNING THE WHEEL

Words and Music by
George Michael and Johnny Douglas

WAITING FOR THAT DAY

Words and Music by
George Michael

Do– do – do do – do do – do do – do do – do – do – do do – do do – do do – do do

194

202

I KNEW YOU WERE WAITING
(FOR ME)

Words and Music by
Dennis Morgan and Simon Climie

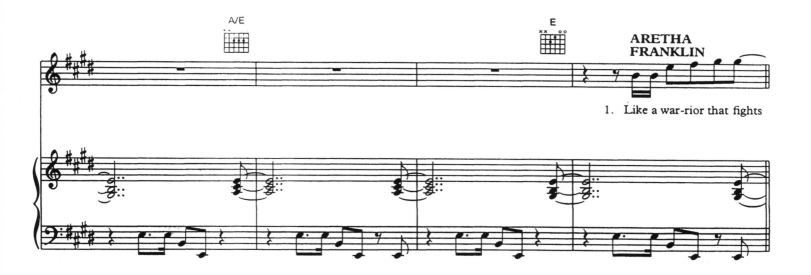

ARETHA
FRANKLIN

1. Like a war-rior that fights

and wins the bat - tle, _____ I know _____ the taste of vic - to - ry.

(2.) I kept on search-ing, sure _____ in time our eyes would meet.

FAITH

Words and Music by
George Michael

SOMEBODY TO LOVE

Words and Music by
Freddie Mercury

220

Find me some-bod-y to love,___ Find me some-bod-y to love,___

Find me some-bod-y to love,___ Find me some-bod-y to love,___

Find me some-bod-y to love.___ Find me some-bod-y to love,___

Find me some-bod-y to love,___ Some-bod-y, some-bod-y, some-bod-y, some-bod-y.

this collection
is dedicated in its entirety to
my mother, Lesley